# Inventi
# Future

## Lisa Thompson

Blake
EDUCATION

Brainwaves Blue
*Inventing the Future*
1 86509 920 1

Copyright © 2005 Blake Publishing
Reprinted 2006

Blake Education Pty Ltd
ABN 50 074 266 023
108 Main Rd
Clayton South VIC 3168
Ph: (03) 9558 4433
Fax: (03) 9558 5433
email: mail@blake.com.au
Visit our website: www.blake.com.au

Series publisher: Katy Pike
Series editors: Sophia Oravecz and Garda Turner
Designer: Cliff Watt
Illustrator: Cliff Watt

Picture credits: p8 Roger Harris/Science Photo
Library; p9 (main) Victor Habbick Visions/Science
Photo Library, (inset) Christian Darkin/Science
Photo Library; pp11, 14 pictures courtesy
NASA/JPL-Caltech; p15 (bottom) APL/Corbis
- Bettmann; p23 AP; p24 APL/Corbis/Haruyoshi
Yamaguchi; p25 (top) picture courtesy NASA;
p26 Peter Rae/Fairfaxphotos; pp27, 28, 29 AP.

Proudly printed in Australia by Printing Creations

# CONTENTS

# Devices of Wonder

**Pass the thing-a-me-jig!**

Gadgets and gizmos solve problems or make life easier. They save time and are clever. Look around your home. The place is full of them! It's hard to live without these handy inventions. How many gadgets have you used today?

# World Travel Gizmos

Gadgets and gizmos helped us find new worlds. Sailors used a **compass** and **sextant** when at sea. These two gadgets made it much easier for sailors to know where they were going and where they had been.

Compasses and sextants have been replaced by modern technology.

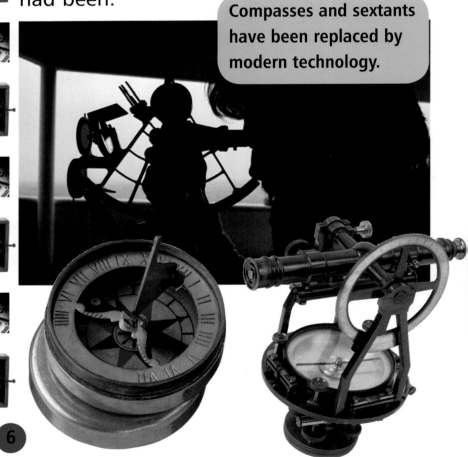

Now we have GPS - the Global Positioning System. This gizmo uses signals from satellites in space. The signals show where you are on Earth. All you have to do is push a button!

With a GPS in your hand, you'll never get lost.

I knew I parked here somewhere!

# Robots to the Rescue

Where else could gadgets and gizmos take us?

By 2020, we will have **nanorobots** in our blood. That's what scientists think. When you are sick, the robots will be injected by a doctor. These little helpers will give you medicine when you need it. They will also swim through your body looking for other signs of sickness. Once their job is finished, the doctor will take the nanorobots out.

**A nanorobot on a strand of hair**

If nanorobots can clean inside our body, they can be used to clean outside too. Imagine – tiny robots all over your teeth, hair and clothes. Nothing has to be washed ever again!

You won't be able to feel nanorobots in your blood or on your body. They are so tiny that they fit onto the top of a pin.

# Traffic Jams in the Sky

Running late for school? Why not hop into your flying car? The American space agency NASA is busy designing cars with wings. The car will come with GPS, so you know where you are. To steer, it will have a joystick. You won't even need a driver's licence! NASA plans to start selling them by 2015. But they aren't cheap - these clever gizmos will cost over $150 000.

The flying car will even have anti-collision technology, so there will be no more accidents.

Hydrobots will be used to explore frozen parts of planets and cold areas, like Antarctica, on Earth.

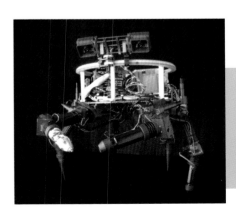

This six-legged robot was developed by NASA to copy the movement of insects.

# Go Go Techno Gizmo

**Smaller, faster, better, stronger —
the world of the modern gizmo.**

Many gizmos use computer chips.
Chips use electricity to do clever things.
Microchips are tiny but hold lots of
information. And they are getting smaller.
That means gizmos are getting faster,
smarter and cheaper.

# A World-changing Gizmo

It all began in 1947. That's when three scientists invented the **transistor**. The three scientists were from the Bell Laboratories. Their names were John Bardeen, Walter Brattain and William Shockley.

Q: What's on the television every night?
A: *The remote control.*

The first transistor was about the size of your thumb. It was made from a paperclip, gold foil, wire and a bit of plastic. Transistors were first used in telephones.

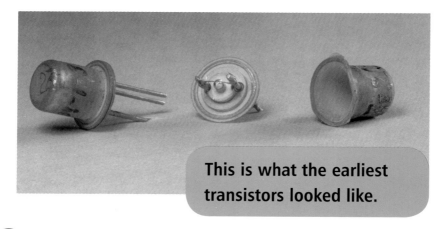

This is what the earliest transistors looked like.

Transistors are in computers, the Internet, mobile phones, TVs, car instrument panels, video cameras, calculators, hand-held games, radar, satellites, night vision technology and all electronics.

TRACKING SUSPECT

The three scientists at Bell Laboratories

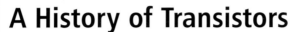

# A History of Transistors

The transistor was an important invention. It meant people could switch electric things on and off quickly. It was also important for future inventions.

Today, PC microchips hold more than three million transistors.

## Transistor Timeline

first pocket-sized transistor radio goes on sale

transistor invented

computer chip developed

| 1947 | 1952 | 1959 |

Today, millions of transistors can be put onto a small microchip. It's so tiny that it can sit on the tip of your little finger!

We wouldn't have made it to space without the transistor.

first pocket calculator developed

first personal computer sold (Apple II)

first CDs go on sale

MP3 music players, DVDs and mobile phones are all common

1970  1977  1982  2004

# How a Microchip Works

A microchip is a thin piece of **silicon**. The transistors have been **etched** onto the microchip. Transistors make up the **microprocessor**.

Microprocessors are the brains inside every computer. They are full of instructions called programs. These programs tell computers what to do.

A chip with lots of transistors can hold more instructions. And it can do more too. A chip can have tens of millions of transistors.

A central processing unit is a microprocessor.

| Name | Date | Transistors |
| --- | --- | --- |
| 8080 | 1974 | 6 000 |
| 80386 | 1985 | 275,000 |
| Pentium 4 | 2004 | 125,000,000 |

You need small gadgets to fix computers.

There are three basic parts to a microprocessor:
1. The program counter – keeps track of which program is being done.
2. Memory – records which commands are to be done.
3. Input/output – the transfer of data to and from the computer from the operator (you).

# What's Next?

**A modern gizmo guru — giz whiz Dr Nakamatsu!**

Dr Nakamatsu is a modern inventor. He holds the world record for the most **patents** and inventions. Dr Nakamatsu has over 3 200 inventions!

# Why Didn't I Think of That?

Dr Nakamatsu's most famous inventions are the CD and the digital watch. He started inventing when he was five. Dr Nakamatsu was 14 when he invented a pump. His mother used it in the kitchen.

Dr Nakamatsu's other inventions include a chair that gets rid of jet lag and Flying Shoes.

Q: What can you make but not see?

A: A noise.

Dr Nakamatsu patented the floppy disc. IBM now owns the technology and pays Dr Nakamatsu for every disc that is bought.

Dr Nakamatsu takes his Flying Shoes for a ride.

# Swimming in Ideas

Dr Nakamatsu often came up with ideas underwater. He invented a notepad that he could use in water. Now he can stay underwater and write down his ideas.

## Awake with ideas

Dr Nakamatsu only sleeps four hours a night. He says the best time for new ideas is between midnight and 4 am. He has two special rooms to help him think. First he goes to the calm room to stop the noise. Then he goes to a room with music and computers. This room makes him think.

Dr Nakamatsu received an award for outstanding services to the community.

Dr Nakamatsu holds over 2 300 patents. In second place for the world's most patents is the American inventor Thomas Edison with 1 093 patents. The next closest competitor holds just 400 patents!

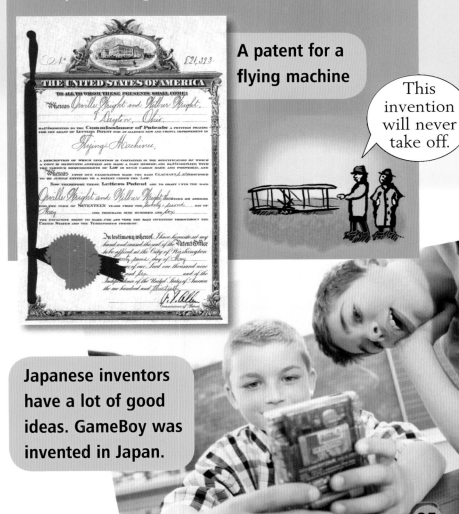

A patent for a flying machine

This invention will never take off.

Japanese inventors have a lot of good ideas. GameBoy was invented in Japan.

# What's that Button do?

Watch out! These gizmos are almost here!

Imagine a necklace that can show video clips. Or a picture frame that will be able to show and send emailed pictures and video clips. Now that's clever!

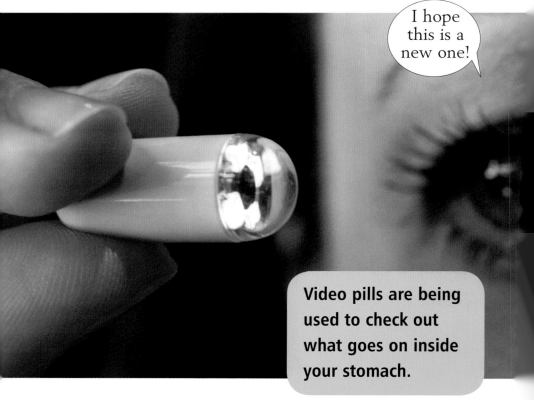

I hope this is a new one!

Video pills are being used to check out what goes on inside your stomach.

# Fingerprint Memory Stick

Don't leave home without one! No more keys, passwords or money to remember. It's smaller than a piece of chewing gum. This stick has your fingerprint on it. You can use it to get into your home, to play games and to buy stuff.

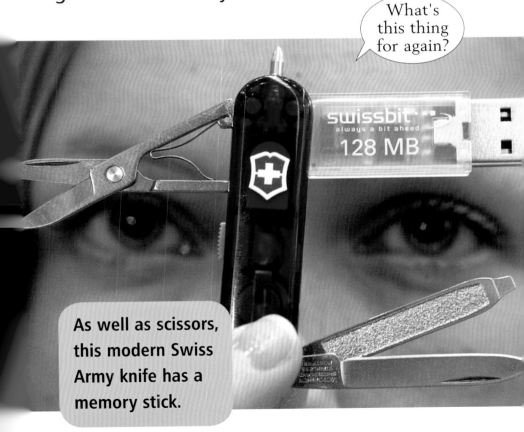

As well as scissors, this modern Swiss Army knife has a memory stick.

# Charged up

How will you keep all these great gizmos **charged**? In your new 'smart jacket' of course! It looks like a normal jacket but it has charges in the lining and the pockets. Your gizmos are charged by the sun as you carry them around!

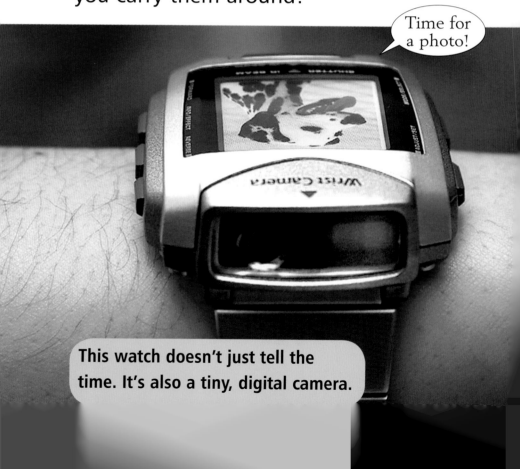

Time for a photo!

This watch doesn't just tell the time. It's also a tiny, digital camera.

# Spy-cool

How about a watch that is also a camera? A Japanese company has invented a watch that can send and receive photos. That's spy cool!

By 2010, a robot will be able to pass school tests. So look out for the school Swot-bot!

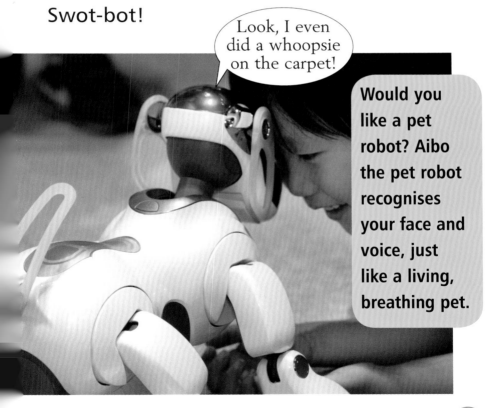

Look, I even did a whoopsie on the carpet!

Would you like a pet robot? Aibo the pet robot recognises your face and voice, just like a living, breathing pet.

# Fact File

Box of widgets

Is your invention a widget? Charles Widge (1874-1937) was an English inventor. He spent most of his life in his garage building strange things called 'widgets'. They all had one thing in common – they were useless!

Tamagotchi was the world's first virtual gizmo pet. In Japanese 'tamago' means egg and 'tomodatchi' means friend so the word means 'egg friend'. It was released in 1996. Tamagotchi was invented by Japanese woman Aki Maita.

Wow, I cooked a microchip!

In the future, a house will have a kitchen where all the gadgets are controlled through the Internet. You can put the kettle on while you're still at work!

# Glossary

| | |
|---|---|
| **charged** | filled with electricity |
| **compass** | an instrument with a magnetic needle which points north |
| **etched** | cut into |
| **microprocessor** | contains the instructions and microchips in a computer |
| **nanorobot** | a tiny robot |
| **patent** | the official right to sell your invention for a set time without being copied |
| **sextant** | an instrument that measures the angles of planets and stars |
| **silicon** | element used in computer parts |
| **transistor** | a device that can switch electric currents on and off at high speed |

# Index